Magic Mates
Meet the Masterpiece

Jane West

RISING★STARS

Rising Stars UK Ltd.
22 Grafton Street, London W1S 4EX
www.risingstars-uk.com

The right of Jane West to be identified as the author of this work
has been asserted by her in accordance with the Copyright, Design
and Patents Act 1988.

Published 2008

Text, design and layout © Rising Stars UK Ltd.

Cover design: Button plc
Illustrator: Stik, Bill Greenhead for Illustration
Text design and typesetting: Andy Wilson
Publisher: Gill Budgell
Editor: Jane Wood

British Library Cataloguing in Publication Data.
A CIP record for this book is available from the British Library

ISBN: 983 1 84680 333 8

Printed in the UK by CPI Bookmarque, Croydon, CR0 4TD

Mixed Sources
Product group from well-managed
forests and other controlled sources
www.fsc.org Cert no. TT-COC-002227
© 1996 Forest Stewardship Council

Contents

Meet the Magic Mates

The Magic Mates are best friends –
but that doesn't mean they're all alike.

Name: *Izzie*

The sporty one: can climb trees, surf and take on the boys at their own game – and win.

Travels by: running!

Loves: trendy tracksuits, open skies and sandy beaches.

Hates: standing still.

Name: *Meena*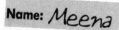

The girly one: uses her mobile for networking and planning her social life.

Travels by: Mum's car (her personal chauffeur).

Loves: pink and her Magic Mates.

Hates: breaking a nail.

Name: Ginger

The ginger one: you don't wanna mess with this feisty gal – the Kung Fu and quick quip queen!

Travels by: push-scooter.

Loves: Jackie Chan and her Magic Mate pals.

Hates: nail extensions.

Name: Jo

The clever one: uses her brains and quick wit to talk her way out of trouble. Sometimes she's a bit too quick.

Travels by: bicycle and is designing a pair of motorised rollerblades.

Loves: Jacqueline Wilson, Cathy Cassidy and Albert Einstein.

Hates: being called 'geek', 'nerd', 'swot' or 'boffin'.

Name: 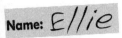Ellie

The fashion-conscious one: can tell her Prada from her Asda and knows how to accessorise.

Travels by: limousine, of course! (But only in her dreams.)

Loves: shopping.

Hates: anything to do with getting dirty; anyone who upsets her Magic Mates.

Name: Yash

The funky punky one: the 'alternative' one of the gang who hugs trees, people and furry animals.

Travels by: skateboard.

Loves: having a good time.

Hates: bullies.

Arty Party

The Magic Mates are on a school trip
to the Nations Gallery in London.
It's fun to have a day out of school,
but how exciting can an art gallery be?
The Magic Mates are about to find out
that an art gallery can be very exciting
indeed.

Yash   Why are we going to look
at a load of boring paintings?
I'd rather go to the zoo
and see the animals.

Ellie   I'd rather go shopping.

Meena   Yes!

Ginger I'd rather go to the park.

Izzie Me too.

Jo Well, I think it will be fun.
We'll see some really famous
paintings worth millions
and millions of pounds.

Ginger How much?!

9

Jo   There's a painter called
            Van Goff. He painted a picture
            of sunflowers, that's worth about
            £20 million.

Yash   Wow!

Meena   It must be very big.

Izzie   Or it's a very good painting.

Ellie   It's a very famous painting.

The Magic Mates walk round the gallery
looking at the different paintings.

Meena   Oh, this one is so sad.
          She was only queen
          for nine days.

Ginger   And then she lost her head.
          Ha, ha, ha!

Ellie	That is so not his colour.
Yash	Why is he holding a flower?
Jo	It says here that this painting was a present for his girlfriend before they got married.
Ginger	No way was he getting married.

Jo   Why not?

Ginger   Because only a mother
could love that face.

Izzie   He does look very stern.

Meena   He needs a haircut.

Yash   Look at this one! The eyes sort of follow you around.

Ginger   It's a bit creepy. I like it.

Izzie   You would!

One of the Warders who look after the paintings comes over to talk to the girls.

Ellie   Do you think that painting is creepy?

Warder   It's one of my favourites. But the eyes do look as if they're following you around. It's not scary when the gallery is full of people. But it's different at night.

Izzie   Why is it different at night?

Warder Well, we still have to guard
the paintings, even at night.
The gallery is never really empty.
But … I shouldn't tell you this …
the gallery is built on
a graveyard.

Ellie   Yeuch!

Meena   Have you ever seen any ghosts?

Warder   No. But sometimes there are strange noises. Footsteps in empty rooms – that sort of thing.

Meena   Well, I'm going to go and find that picture of the sunflowers. That sounds like a much nicer painting.

Jo   I'll go with you. I really want to see it, too.

Ellie   We'll meet you in the shop. Don't forget, the gallery will close soon.

Ginger Don't let the ghosts get you! Ha, ha, ha!

The Sunflowers

Meena and Jo walk through the gallery.
There's no one else around.
Everyone has gone home.

Meena   We'll have to hurry.
              They'll be closing up soon.

Jo   I think it's just in the next room.

The girls stand in front of Van Goff's famous painting.

Meena   Oh, it's so pretty!

Jo   It's so bright and yellow. It's like he's painted it with sunshine.

Meena   I know what you mean.
But it's much smaller
than I was expecting.

Jo   It says here that he was painting
the flowers to go in his
friend's room.

Meena   That's a nice idea.
I'd like that painting in my room.

Jo   Well, unless you've got
£20 million, you'd better buy
a poster of it instead.

Meena   Good plan.
I hope the shop is still open.

But the girls are too late. The lights go off
and the gallery is closed. The girls
are alone in the gloomy old art gallery.

Art Attack!

Meena   Oh no!

Jo   Don't worry. We'll go back the way we came. We'll meet the others outside.

But it isn't easy for Meena and Jo to find their way in the dark. Soon they are lost.

Meena I think we've already been
through this room.
I remember that painting
staring at me.

Jo Oh dear. I think you're right.
It's hard to find the way
in the dark.

Meena   Where are all the Warders?
The one we met said he guarded
the paintings at night,
but we haven't seen anyone.

Jo   Don't worry. The others will
have missed us by now.
They'll send some Warders
to look for us.

The girls jump when they hear
a loud noise.

Meena   What was that?

Jo   I don't know.

Meena   Do you think it was a ghost?

Jo   It's too noisy to be a ghost.

Meena   It must be one of the Warders.
Let's ask them to show us
the way out.

Jo   Good idea.

Meena   I hope it's not too far –
my new shoes are rubbing
my feet.

The girls walk towards the noise.
Suddenly, they recognise where they are.
They're back in the Van Goff room,
but the painting of the sunflowers
is missing. The frame is empty!

Meena   Look! The painting has gone!

Jo   Someone has stolen it!

4

Thief!

The girls are locked in the art gallery at night and a thief has stolen Van Goff's famous painting of sunflowers. What will they do next?

Meena   We have to tell someone that the painting has been stolen.

Jo   We have to get out of here first!

Meena   How? We've been going in circles.

Jo   I've got an idea.

Meena   Good!

Jo   Let's follow the thief.

Meena   Whaaaaat?! No way!

Jo   Think about it. If we try and get out by ourselves we could be wandering around all night. The thief must know the way out. We might be able to stop him stealing the painting.

Meena and Jo creep along in the dark.
The thief is noisy and easy to follow.

Meena   He's making a lot of noise
for a thief.

Jo   Yes, he is. And I don't understand
why we haven't seen any Warders.
Oh! I can see the thief now –
look over there.

The girls follow the thief to a large room.
He opens it with a big key. Inside are all
the Warders. They have been tied up.

Jo   Now we know why we haven't
seen any Warders.

Meena   This thief is clever.

Jo   Not clever enough. Look,
there's a fire alarm on the wall.
If we can reach that …

Meena … we'll be able to set off
the alarm and the police
will come. Brilliant!

Jo It's quite high up.
I'll have to stand on a chair.

Meena If you do that the thief
will hear you moving the chair!

Jo You're right. *You'll* have to
reach the alarm. I'll give you
a piggyback.

Meena I still can't reach it. I'll have to get on your shoulders.

Meena gets on to Jo's shoulders.
It's a bit wobbly but at least she can reach the alarm now.

Thief   Oi! Where did you two girls come from?

Jo   Meena, quick!
Ring the alarm.

Thief   Get down now!

Meena   I've done it! Aaaaaagh!

The thief pushes Jo and Meena falls off.
It's too late for the thief – Meena has
set off the alarm.

A Painting Restored

The alarm bell is ringing and Meena
and Jo are lying on the floor.
The thief looks worried.

Thief   How do I get out of here?

Jo   We don't know. We were lost
so we followed you.

Thief   I thought I knew the way out.
But I heard a loud noise
so I ran away.

Meena   If that wasn't you making
that noise, who was it?

At that moment the police arrive.
They arrest the thief and take him away.

Warder Well done, girls. If it hadn't been for you the Nations Gallery would have lost a priceless painting.

Jo There's one thing that puzzles me.

Warder What's that?

Jo The thief said he ran away when he heard a loud noise, but there was no one else here.

Warder The gallery is a strange place at night. When you are alone in the dark, your eyes can play tricks on you. Sometimes it feels like you're being watched – but it's just the paintings. You must have imagined it.

Jo isn't so sure, but everyone is just glad that the painting is safe. The Warder makes sure that the Van Goff painting is put back in its frame.

Jo   I'm glad we saved the painting.

Meena   Yes, and I'm glad the police
came so quickly. I didn't like
lying on the floor – I bruised
my knee when I fell down.

Jo   They say you have to suffer
for your art.

Meena   Ha ha. Ouch!
Ha ha! Ouch!
Ha ha!

About the Author

Jane West:

 lives by the beach in Cornwall

 likes taking her dog Pip paddling
in the sea

loves bodyboarding

has worked in a bookshop, a school,
and in the real National Gallery
in London. She says it's true about
the National Gallery being built
on a graveyard. And it's true that it's
a very creepy place to be at night
when all the visitors have left …

Now she's a writer, and has had great fun
writing about the Magic Mates. She hopes
you liked reading about them.

The Author's Favourite Painting

I really like the painting by Andrea Solario (1465–1524) called 'A Man With a Pink'. It looks very like the picture opposite. I bet he's really a softy! You can see this painting in the National Gallery in London.

But my favourite painting is 'The Rain It Raineth Every Day' by Norman Garstin (1847–1926). It reminds me of wet holidays by the sea when I was a little girl. You can see this painting in the Penlee Gallery in Penzance.

Vincent Van Gogh

 Vincent Van Gogh
was a real painter who lived
from 1853 until 1890. He was born
in the Netherlands but also visited Britain.

 In this story is name is spelled 'Goff'
because that's how you say 'Gogh'.

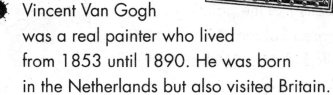 Van Gogh painted several pictures
of sunflowers to decorate a room
for his friend, the painter Paul Gaugin,
so it would be full of sunny flowers.

'The Sunflowers' in the National Gallery
really is worth about £20 million. But, sadly,
Van Gogh was very poor when he died.
He didn't sell any paintings while
he was alive – except to his brother, Theo.

The National Gallery

 The National Gallery opened in 1824.

It has over 2300 paintings.

The gallery moved to its home in Trafalgar Square in 1838.

During the Second World War, many paintings were evacuated to deep mines in Wales. This was safer than leaving them in London to be bombed.

It is free to go inside the gallery.

The paintings are owned by the British public.

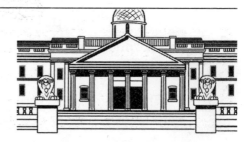

Artijokes!

Why are vampires so good at art?

They're good at drawing blood!

Van Gogh's sunflowers were arrested
by the police for murder.
They said they'd been framed!

Art Lingo

Canvas   Most artists paint on a rough material called 'canvas' rather than on paper.

Cartoon   Not a film made from drawings, but a rough sketch made by the artist before beginning a painting.

Egg tempera   A water-based paint made with the yolk of an egg. Yes, really!

Fresco   Painting on to wet plaster. The famous painting 'The Last Supper' by Leonardo da Vinci was made in this way.

Impressionism   A name given to painting in the 1870s. Painters who used this style liked to give an impression of sunshine or light. This was a new style: before, most paintings were more like photographs.

Masterpiece   A really great painting.

Primary colours   Red, yellow and blue. You can mix every colour you need from these – except white!

Artful Quiz!

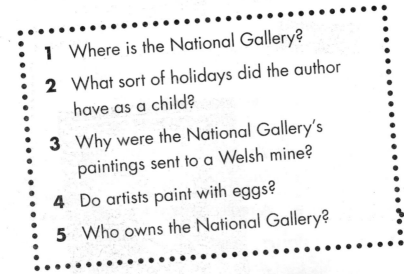

1 Where is the National Gallery?

2 What sort of holidays did the author have as a child?

3 Why were the National Gallery's paintings sent to a Welsh mine?

4 Do artists paint with eggs?

5 Who owns the National Gallery?

How did you score?

0–1 More 'Oh no' than 'fresco'…

2–3 You'd sell more paintings than Van Gogh did when he was alive!

4–5 If you were a painting, you'd be a masterpiece!

Magic Mates

RISING ★ STARS